Written Calculation Subtraction
Answers

Schofield&Sims

Introduction for parents and teachers

This book provides correct answers to all the questions in the Pupil Book **Written Calculation: Subtraction** (ISBN 978 07217 1267 3), including those contained in each **Check-up test** and **Final test**.

Which pupils will benefit most from Written Calculation: Subtraction?

Subtraction is for pupils who already understand the value of digits in numbers. They are able to identify the units digit in a four-digit number such as 5468. They also know the values of the other digits, including tens, hundreds and thousands. Pupils should also be experienced in adding and subtracting single-digit numbers and should know their bonds to 20 (for example, $7 + 8$, $9 - 5$, $14 - 7$). Pupils who know these well will find written subtraction easier than those who have to work them out. For this reason, pupils who have not yet memorised number bonds may find it useful temporarily to refer to a list of number facts – downloadable from the Schofield & Sims website. This will allow them to focus on the procedures of the written method. Once the pupils are familiar with the facts, they will no longer need the list.

How should the Pupil Book be used?

Pupils should work consecutively through all 18 'steps', if they are to become fully proficient in the most important stages of the learning process. At the end of each step are **Problem solving** questions. Pupils record their workings onto the grids provided and also write their answers in the book. Make sure that each pupil completes the **self-evaluation** rating at the end of each step by ticking 'Easy', 'OK' or 'Difficult'. Review each pupil's rating against his or her score for that step, and give support to pupils who are struggling. The final steps in the book extend more able pupils and take them beyond the statutory aspects of written subtraction, requiring them to work with larger numbers and decimals, for example. **Check-up tests** and a **Final test** help you to monitor progress, and this book of **Answers** makes marking simple and quick. Use the **conversion chart** at the end of each test to quickly convert the pupil's score to a percentage that can be recorded and used to measure progress.

Please note: Pupils will require additional squared paper to help them complete some of the pages in the Pupil Book.

The separate **Written Calculation: Teacher's Guide** (ISBN 978 07217 1278 9) contains full teaching notes and assessment resources. The **Teacher's Resource Book** (ISBN 978 07217 1300 7) contains photocopiable resources. Both cover the whole series and provide the teacher with valuable guidance and resources to support the teaching of written calculation. For free downloads and for further details on all the other **Written Calculation** books, visit **www.schofieldandsims.co.uk**

Published by Schofield & Sims Ltd, Dogley Mill, Fenay Bridge, Huddersfield HD8 0NQ, UK Tel 01484 607080 www.schofieldandsims.co.uk

First published in 2015. Copyright © Schofield & Sims Ltd, 2015.

Authors: **Hilary Koll and Steve Mills**

Hilary Koll and Steve Mills have asserted their moral rights under the Copyright, Designs and Patents Act, 1988, to be identified as the authors of this work.

British Library Cataloguing in Publication Data

A catalogue record for this book is available from the British Library.

All rights reserved. No part of this publication may be reproduced, stored in a retrieval system, or transmitted in any form or by any means, electronic, mechanical, photocopying, recording or otherwise, without either the prior permission of the publisher or a licence permitting restricted copying in the United Kingdom issued by the Copyright Licensing Agency Limited, Saffron House, 6–10 Kirby Street, London EC1N 8TS.

Commissioned by **Carolyn Richardson Publishing Services (www.publiserve.co.uk)**

Design by **Ledgard Jepson Ltd**

Cover illustration by **Joe Hance (joehance.co.uk)**

Printed in the UK by **Wyndeham Gait Ltd, Grimsby, Lincolnshire**

ISBN 978 07217 1273 4

Contents

Step 1: Two-digit subtraction no exchange

When learning written subtraction, it is important to know how to set numbers out vertically with the correct digits in the correct columns. Here, 87 and 36 are correctly written under the Tens and Units headings.

What to do

87 – 36 = ?

	T	U
	8	7
–	3	6

1 Set out the numbers in the correct columns with one digit in each square.

2 Always start at the right-hand side, with the units column! Subtract the bottom digit from the top digit. 7 – 6 = 1

	T	U
	8	7
–	3	6
		1

3 Next move to the left and look at the digits in the tens column. Subtract the bottom digit from the top digit. 8 – 3 = 5

4 Finally, look at the answer and check whether it seems a sensible answer. You can add the answer to the number subtracted to see if it gives you the top number. 51 + 36 = 87 Yes, this is correct.

	T	U
	8	7
–	3	6
	5	1

Now you try

1 96 – 44 = ?

	T	U
	9	6
–	4	4
	5	2

2 75 – 31 = ?

	T	U
	7	5
–	3	1
	4	4

3 68 – 42 = ?

	T	U
	6	8
–	4	2
	2	6

4 58 – 27 = ?

	T	U
	5	8
–	2	7
	3	1

5 87 – 24 = ?

	T	U
	8	7
–	2	4
	6	3

6 79 – 46 = ?

	T	U
	7	9
–	4	6
	3	3

More practice

Set out these questions yourself to answer them.

7 78 − 24 = ?

	T	U
	7	8
−	2	4
	5	4

8 95 − 33 = ?

	T	U
	9	5
−	3	3
	6	2

9 88 − 46 = ?

	T	U
	8	8
−	4	6
	4	2

10 Check your answers above by adding.

54 + 24 = 78   62 + 33 = 95   42 + 46 = 88

Problem solving

11 A shop had a shelf with 89 tins on it. If 43 of the tins are bought, how many tins remain on the shelf?

```
   8 9
 − 4 3
 ─────
   4 6
```
46

12 Mrs Smith only has 78p in her purse. She takes out 45p to pay in a car park. How much money is left in the purse?

```
   7 8
 − 4 5
 ─────
   3 3
```
33p

13 The height of Jo's dog is 93cm. The height of Jo's cat is 23cm. How much taller is Jo's dog than Jo's cat?

```
   9 3
 − 2 3
 ─────
   7 0
```
70cm

14 David weighed 86kg before going on a diet. After his diet he weighs 72kg. How many kilograms did he lose?

```
   8 6
 − 7 2
 ─────
   1 4
```
14kg

How did I find Step 1?   Easy   OK   Difficult

Step 2: Three-digit subtraction no exchange

For three-digit numbers, work in the same way. Make sure the numbers are set out in the correct columns in the same way. Here, 576 and 143 are correctly written under the Hundreds, Tens and Units headings.

What to do

$576 - 143 = ?$

H	T	U
5	7	6
− 1	4	3

1   Set out the numbers in the correct columns with one digit in each square.

	5	7	6
−	1	4	3
			3

2   Always start at the right-hand side, with the units column! Subtract the bottom digit from the top digit. $6 - 3 = 3$

	5	7	6
−	1	4	3
		3	3

3   Next, move to the left and look at the digits in the tens column. Subtract the bottom digit from the top digit. $7 - 4 = 3$

	5	7	6
−	1	4	3
	4	3	3

4   Then move to the left again and subtract the bottom digit from the top digit in the hundreds column. $5 - 1 = 4$

5   Finally, look at the answer and check whether it seems a sensible answer. $433 + 143$ is 576, which is correct!

Now you try

1 $489 - 144 = ?$

H	T	U
4	8	9
− 1	4	4
3	4	5

2 $575 - 214 = ?$

H	T	U
5	7	5
− 2	1	4
3	6	1

3 $859 - 435 = ?$

H	T	U
8	5	9
− 4	3	5
4	2	4

4 $583 - 271 = ?$

H	T	U
5	8	3
− 2	7	1
3	1	2

5 $837 - 224 = ?$

H	T	U
8	3	7
− 2	2	4
6	1	3

6 $794 - 464 = ?$

H	T	U
7	9	4
− 4	6	4
3	3	0

More practice

Set out these questions yourself to answer them.

7 475 – 123 = ?

	H	T	U
	4	7	5
–	1	2	3
	3	5	2

8 888 – 447 = ?

	H	T	U
	8	8	8
–	4	4	7
		4	4	1

9 739 – 127 = ?

	H	T	U
	7	3	9
–	1	2	7
		6	1	2

10 967 – 264 = ?

	H	T	U
	9	6	7
–	2	6	4
	7	0	3

11 469 – 327 = ?

	H	T	U
	4	6	9
–	3	2	7
	1	4	2

12 573 – 402 = ?

	H	T	U
	5	7	3
–	4	0	2
	1	7	1

Problem solving

13 A farmer had 678 sheep. She sells 315 of them at market. How many sheep has she now?

```
    6  7  8
 -  3  1  5
 _____
    3  6  3        363
```

14 Kim had £468 in a bank account. She took out £225. How much money stayed in the bank account?

```
    4  6  8
 -  2  2  5
 _____
    2  4  3        £243
```

15 Two numbers have a difference of 733. If the larger number is 969, what is the smaller number?

```
    9  6  9
 -  7  3  3
 _____
    2  3  6        236
```

16 687 people went to a football match. 136 of them left early. How many people were there at the end?

```
    6  8  7
 -  1  3  6
 _____
    5  5  1        551
```

How did I find Step 2? ☐ Easy ☐ OK ☐ Difficult

Step 3: Three-digit subtraction exchanging 1 ten for 10 units

These questions have one digit in the bottom number that is larger than the digit above it.

See here that the 8 is larger than the 3 above it!

H	T	U
5	7	3
− 1	4	8

What to do

$573 - 148 = ?$

1 You can't take 8 away from 3 so you must exchange ten from the column to its left. Cross out the 7 tens and write one fewer above it. One fewer than 7 is 6.

	6	
5	7̶	3
− 1	4	8

2 Now, take the ten you have exchanged and write it in the units column, so instead of 3 units you now have 10 + 3 = 13. Now you can take away 8 from 13 and get the answer 5.

	6	
5	7̶	¹3
− 1	4	8
		5

3 Then complete the rest of the subtraction as normal, working from right to left.

	6	
5	7̶	¹3
− 1	4	8
4	2	5

Now you try

1
	6	
4	7̶	¹3
− 1	3	8
3	3	5

2
	8	
7	9̶	¹3
− 2	3	6
5	5	7

3
	4	
8	5̶	¹2
− 4	1	5
4	3	7

4
	7	
7	8̶	¹4
− 2	5	7
5	2	7

5
	4	
6	5̶	¹3
− 2	1	9
4	3	4

6
	7	
4	8̶	¹2
− 1	6	7
3	1	5

7
	6	
8	7̶	¹6
− 5	5	7
3	1	9

8
	2	
9	3̶	¹4
− 6	1	9
3	1	5

9
	7	
8	8̶	¹1
− 7	2	7
1	5	4

More practice

10
$$
\begin{array}{r}
4\ \overset{6}{\cancel{7}}\ {}^{1}5 \\
-\ 1\ 4\ 7 \\
\hline
3\ 2\ 8 \\
\hline
\end{array}
$$

11
$$
\begin{array}{r}
5\ \overset{8}{\cancel{9}}\ {}^{1}3 \\
-\ 2\ 8\ 6 \\
\hline
3\ 0\ 7 \\
\hline
\end{array}
$$

12
$$
\begin{array}{r}
6\ \overset{1}{\cancel{2}}\ {}^{1}4 \\
-\ 4\ 1\ 8 \\
\hline
2\ 0\ 6 \\
\hline
\end{array}
$$

Set out these questions yourself to answer them.

13 475 − 128 = ?

H	T	U
	6	
4	$\cancel{7}$	¹5
− 1	2	8
3	4	7

14 886 − 447 = ?

H	T	U
	7	
8	$\cancel{8}$	¹6
− 4	4	7
4	3	9

15 730 − 127 = ?

H	T	U
	2	
7	$\cancel{3}$	¹0
− 1	2	7
6	0	3

16 967 − 259 = ?

H	T	U
	5	
9	$\cancel{6}$	¹7
− 2	5	9
7	0	8

17 465 − 327 = ?

H	T	U
	5	
4	$\cancel{6}$	¹5
− 3	2	7
1	3	8

18 573 − 406 = ?

H	T	U
	6	
5	$\cancel{7}$	¹3
− 4	0	6
1	6	7

Problem solving

19 Subtract 327 from 574.

$$
\begin{array}{r}
5\ \overset{6}{\cancel{7}}\ {}^{1}4 \\
-\ 3\ 2\ 7 \\
\hline
2\ 4\ 7 \\
\hline
\end{array}
$$

247

20 Joe had £465 in a bank account. He took out £228. How much money was left in the bank account?

$$
\begin{array}{r}
4\ \overset{5}{\cancel{6}}\ {}^{1}5 \\
-\ 2\ 2\ 8 \\
\hline
2\ 3\ 7 \\
\hline
\end{array}
$$

£237

How did I find Step 3? ☐ Easy ☐ OK ☐ Difficult

Step 4: Three-digit subtraction exchanging
1 hundred for 10 tens

As for Step 3, these questions have one digit in the bottom number that is larger than the digit above it, but this time it is the tens digit.

See here that the 8 is larger than the 3 above it!

H	T	U
5	3	6
− 1	8	5

What to do

$536 - 185 = ?$

H	T	U
5	3	6
− 1	8	5

1 Start with the units. Subtract 5 from 6 leaving 1.

H	T	U
5	3	6
− 1	8	5
		1

2 Then move left to the tens. Because you can't take 8 away from 3, you must exchange one hundred from the column to its left. Cross out the 5 hundreds and write one fewer above it. One fewer than 5 is 4.

3 Next take the hundred you have exchanged and write it in the tens column, so instead of 3 tens you now have 10 tens + 3 tens = 13 tens. Now you can take away 8 from 13 to get 5.

	4		
	5̶	¹3	6
−	1	8	5
		5	1

4 Finally, look at the hundreds column. Subtract 1 hundred from the 4 hundreds that are left to give 3 hundreds.

	4		
	5̶	¹3	6
−	1	8	5
	3	5	1

Now you try

1

	4		
	5̶	¹2	3
−	1	4	2
	3	8	1

2

	6		
	7̶	¹4	8
−	2	7	6
	4	7	2

3

	7		
	8̶	¹3	9
−	4	9	5
	3	4	4

4

	6		
	7̶	¹5	4
−	2	8	2
	4	7	2

5

	5		
	6̶	¹5	6
−	2	8	6
	3	7	0

6

	3		
	4̶	¹6	8
−	1	7	7
	2	9	1

More practice

7
```
      3
    4 '0  9
 –  1  4  7
 ─────────
    2  6  2
```

8
```
      7
    8 '1  8
 –  2  8  6
 ─────────
    5  3  2
```

9
```
      5
    6 '4  9
 –  4  6  8
 ─────────
    1  8  1
```

Set out these questions yourself to answer them.

10 477 – 193 = ?

H	T	U
3		
4	'7	7
– 1	9	3
2	8	4

11 826 – 474 = ?

H	T	U
7		
8	'2	6
– 4	7	4
3	5	2

12 736 – 186 = ?

H	T	U
6		
7	'3	6
– 1	8	6
5	5	0

13 967 – 283 = ?

H	T	U
8		
9	'6	7
– 2	8	3
6	8	4

14 415 – 321 = ?

H	T	U
3		
4	'1	5
– 3	2	1
	9	4

15 543 – 452 = ?

H	T	U
4		
5	'4	3
– 4	5	2
	9	1

Problem solving

16 Use subtraction to find the difference between 547 and 175.

```
      4
    5 '4  7
 –  1  7  5
 ─────────
    3  7  2
```
372

17 A safari park has 636 animals. If 184 of them are monkeys, how many of the animals are not monkeys?

```
      5
    6 '3  6
 –  1  8  4
 ─────────
    4  5  2
```
452

| **How did I find Step 4?** | ☐ Easy | ☐ OK | ☐ Difficult |

Step 5: Three-digit subtraction exchanging once

On these pages, you must decide when to exchange. Sometimes you will need to exchange a ten and sometimes you will need to exchange a hundred. Look for when a digit in the bottom number is larger than the digit above it.

What to do

$773 - 255 = ?$

H   T   U

	7	⁶⁄X̶	¹3
−	2	5	5

1. Start with the units. Is the bottom digit larger than the top digit? Is 5 larger than 3? Yes. So you must exchange a ten.

2. If the lower digit is larger you must exchange one from the column to its left. Here, exchange 1 ten. Cross out the 7 tens and write one fewer above it. One fewer than 7 is 6.

	7	⁶⁄X̶	¹3
−	2	5	5
			8

3. Next, take the ten you have exchanged and write it in the units column, so instead of 3 units you now have $10 + 3 = 13$ units.

4. Now you can take away 5 from 13 to get 8.

5. Continue with the subtraction in the same way, working from right to left.

	7	⁶⁄X̶	¹3
−	2	5	5
	5	1	8

Now you try

1

	⁷⁄8̶	¹1	5
−	1	4	2
	6	7	3

2

	6	³⁄4̶	¹3
−	2	2	6
	4	1	7

3

	⁷⁄8̶	¹3	6
−	2	6	5
	5	7	1

4

	⁶⁄7̶	¹5	5
−	2	9	2
	4	6	3

5

	6	⁵⁄6̶	¹6
−	2	5	8
	4	0	8

6

	4	³⁄4̶	¹8
−	1	2	9
	3	1	9

More practice

7

	3		
	~~4~~	¹0	8
–	2	5	3
	1	5	5

8

		8	
	8	~~9~~	¹1
–	2	8	6
	6	0	5

9

	7		
	~~8~~	¹4	5
–	7	8	3
		6	2

Set out these questions yourself to answer them.

10 592 – 245 = ?

	H	T	U
		8	
	5	~~9~~	¹2
–	2	4	5
	3	4	7

11 746 – 284 = ?

	H	T	U
	6		
	~~7~~	¹4	6
–	2	8	4
	4	6	2

12 736 – 685 = ?

	H	T	U
	6		
	~~7~~	¹3	6
–	6	8	5
		5	1

13 925 – 317 = ?

	H	T	U
		1	
	9	~~2~~	¹5
–	3	1	7
	6	0	8

14 885 – 306 = ?

	H	T	U
		7	
	8	~~8~~	¹5
–	3	0	6
	5	7	9

15 537 – 252 = ?

	H	T	U
	4		
	~~5~~	¹3	7
–	2	5	2
	2	8	5

Problem solving

16 A plane has 697 passengers. If 348 of them are male, how many are female?

		8	
	6	~~9~~	¹7
–	3	4	8
	3	4	9

349

17 A skyscraper is 243m tall. It stands next to a cathedral that is 171m tall. How much taller is the skyscraper than the cathedral?

	1		
	~~2~~	¹4	3
–	1	7	1
		7	2

72m

How did I find Step 5? ☐ Easy ☐ OK ☐ Difficult

Check-up test 1 Two- and three-digit subtraction, including one exchange

Step 1

1 79 − 46 = ?

```
    7  9
-   4  6
    3  3
```

2 57 − 23 = ?

```
    5  7
-   2  3
    3  4
```

3 89 − 24 = ?

```
    8  9
-   2  4
    6  5
```

Step 2

4 593 − 251 = ?

```
    5  9  3
-   2  5  1
    3  4  2
```

5 737 − 234 = ?

```
    7  3  7
-   2  3  4
    5  0  3
```

6 794 − 464 = ?

```
    7  9  4
-   4  6  4
    3  3  0
```

Step 3

7 934 − 518 = ?

```
       2
    9  3  ¹4
-   5  1   8
    4  1   6
```

8 771 − 147 = ?

```
          6
    7  7  ¹1
-   1  4   7
    6  2   4
```

9 876 − 128 = ?

```
          6
    8  7  ¹6
-   1  2   8
    7  4   8
```

Step 4

10 468 − 174 = ?

```
       3
    4  ¹6  8
-   1   7  4
    2   9  4
```

11 649 − 468 = ?

```
       5
    6  ¹4  9
-   4   6  8
    1   8  1
```

12 614 − 521 = ?

```
       5
    6  ¹1  4
-   5   2  1
        9  3
```

Step 5

13 692 – 245 = ?

		8	
	6	$\cancel{9}$	^{1}2
–	2	4	5
	4	4	7

14 726 – 683 = ?

		6	
	$\cancel{7}$	^{1}2	6
–	6	8	3
		4	3

15 706 – 385 = ?

		6	
	$\cancel{7}$	^{1}0	6
–	3	8	5
	3	2	1

☐ 13
☐ 14
☐ 15

Steps 1 to 5 mixed

Use the grid below for working.

16 Find the difference between 356 and 588.

232

☐ 16

17 A farmer had 693 cows. He sells 374 of them. How many cows has he now?

319

☐ 17

18 Subtract 281 from 457.

176

☐ 18

19 Find the difference between 953 and 272.

681

☐ 19

16)

		5	8	8
	–	3	5	6
		2	3	2

17)

		6	$\cancel{9}$ ^{8}	^{1}3
	–	3	7	4
		3	1	9

18)

		$\cancel{4}$ ^{3}	^{1}5	7
	–	2	8	1
		1	7	6

19)

		$\cancel{9}$ ^{8}	^{1}5	3
	–	2	7	2
		6	8	1

Total test score

Score	1	2	3	4	5	6	7	8	9	10	11	12	13	14	15	16	17	18	19
%	5	11	16	21	26	32	37	42	47	53	58	63	68	74	79	84	89	95	100

19

Step 6: Four-digit subtraction exchanging 1 thousand for 10 hundreds

As for previous steps, these questions have one digit in the bottom number that is larger than the digit above it, but this time it is the hundreds digit.

See here that the 8 is larger than the 1 above it.

Th	H	T	U
	6	1	8	7
−	1	8	2	3

What to do

$6187 - 1823 = ?$

1 Start with the units. $7 - 3 = 4$

2 Move left to the tens. $8 - 2 = 6$

Th	H	T	U
	6	1	8	7
−	1	8	2	3
			6	4

3 Then move to the hundreds. Because you can't take 8 away from 1, you must exchange 1 thousand from the column to its left. Cross out the 6 thousands and write one fewer above it. One fewer than 6 is 5.

	5			
	6̶	1	8	7
−	1	8	2	3
			6	4

4 Next, take the thousand you have exchanged and write it in the hundreds column, so instead of 1 hundred you now have 10 hundreds + 1 hundred = 11 hundreds.

	5			
	6̶	¹1	8	7
−	1	8	2	3
		3	6	4

5 Now, you can take away 8 from 11 to get 3.

6 Finally, look at the thousands column. Subtract 1 thousand from the 5 thousands that are left to give 4 thousands.

	5			
	6̶	¹1	8	7
−	1	8	2	3
4	3	6	4

Now you try

1

	7			
	8̶	¹3	6	8
−	4	9	4	2
	3	4	2	6

2

	3			
	4̶	¹5	9	7
−	1	8	1	2
	2	7	8	5

3

	5			
	6̶	¹4	8	4
−	5	9	8	3
		5	0	1

4

	6			
	7̶	¹2	5	4
−	3	3	2	4
	3	9	3	0

More practice

Set out these questions yourself to answer them.

5   7598 – 2644 = ?

	Th	H	T	U
	⁶7̶	¹5	9	8
–	2	6	4	4
	4	9	5	4

6   8036 – 4514 = ?

	Th	H	T	U
	⁷8̶	¹0	3	6
–	4	5	1	4
	3	5	2	2

7   6483 – 5873 = ?

	Th	H	T	U
	⁵6̶	¹4	8	3
–	5	8	7	3
		6	1	0

8   9585 – 6664 = ?

	Th	H	T	U
	⁸9̶	¹5	8	5
–	6	6	6	4
	2	9	2	1

Problem solving

9   Kim had £6747 in a bank account.
She took out £1835 to buy a car.
How much money is left in the account?

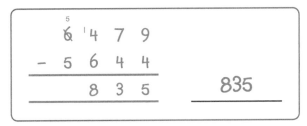

```
    ⁵6̶ ¹7  4  7
 –   1  8  3  5
     4  9  1  2        £4912
```

10   A car park has 6479 parking spaces.
If 5644 are empty, how many are filled?

```
    ⁵6̶ ¹4  7  9
 –   5  6  4  4
        8  3  5        835
```

| **How did I find Step 6?** | ☐ Easy | ☐ OK | ☐ Difficult |

Step 7: Four-digit subtraction exchanging a ten and a thousand

For the questions in this step, you will need to exchange twice. In both the units and hundreds columns, the digit in the bottom number is larger than the digit above it. Here, 9 is larger than the 4 above it and 5 is larger than the 1 above it.

Th	H	T	U
	6	1	8	4
−	1	5	3	9

What to do

6184 − 1539 = ?

1 Start with the units. 9 is larger than 4 so exchange from the tens. Cross out the 8 and write one fewer above it. One fewer than 8 is 7. Next, take the ten you exchanged and write it in the units column, so instead of 4 you now have 10 + 4 = 14 units. Then subtract. 14 − 9 = 5

Th	H	T(7)	U
	6	1	8	¹4
−	1	5	3	9
			4	5

2 Move left to the tens. 7 − 3 = 4

3 Then move to the hundreds. Because you can't take 5 away from 1, exchange 1 thousand. Cross out the 6 thousands and write one fewer above it. One fewer than 6 is 5. Take the thousand and write it in the hundreds column, so instead of 1 hundred you now have 10 hundreds + 1 hundred = 11 hundreds. 11 − 5 = 6

Th(5)	H	T(7)	U
6̶	¹1	8	¹4
− 1	5	3	9
	6	4	5

4 Finally, look at the thousands column. Subtract 1 thousand from the 5 thousands that are left to give 4 thousands.

Th(5)	H	T(7)	U
6̶	¹1	8	¹4
− 1	5	3	9
4	6	4	5

Now you try

1

(7)		(5)	
8̶	¹3	6̶	¹0
− 4	9	4	5
3	4	1	5

2

	(3)		(3)
4	¹5	4̶	¹7
− 1	8	1	8
2	7	2	9

3

(8)		(7)	
9̶	¹4	8̶	¹4
− 5	9	7	7
3	5	0	7

4

	(6)		(4)
7̶	¹2	5̶	¹2
− 6	3	2	9
	9	2	3

More practice

5

$$
\begin{array}{r}
{}^{6}\!\!\not{7}\; {}^{1}5\; 8\; {}^{7}\!{}^{1}0 \\
-\;6\; 9\; 3\; 8 \\
\hline
6\; 4\; 2
\end{array}
$$

6

$$
\begin{array}{r}
{}^{5}\!\not{6}\; 3\; {}^{0}\!\!\not{1}\; {}^{1}2 \\
-\;2\; 6\; 0\; 4 \\
\hline
3\; 7\; 0\; 8
\end{array}
$$

Set out these questions yourself to answer them.

7 8272 – 4756 = ?

Th	H	T	U
$^{7}\not{8}$	$^{1}2$	$^{6}\not{7}$	$^{1}2$
– 4	7	5	6
3	5	1	6

8 9190 – 7614 = ?

Th	H	T	U
$^{8}\not{9}$	$^{1}1$	$^{8}\not{9}$	$^{1}0$
– 7	6	1	4
1	5	7	6

Problem solving

9 Paul's income last year was £8265. This year it was £9171. How much more did he earn this year?

$$
\begin{array}{r}
{}^{8}\!\not{9}\; {}^{1}1\; {}^{6}\!\not{7}\; {}^{1}1 \\
-\;8\; 2\; 6\; 5 \\
\hline
9\; 0\; 6
\end{array}
$$

£906

10 A traffic survey counted 4729 vehicles driving west and 6295 driving east along a road. How many more were driving east than west?

$$
\begin{array}{r}
{}^{5}\!\not{6}\; {}^{1}2\; {}^{8}\!\not{9}\; {}^{1}5 \\
-\;4\; 7\; 2\; 9 \\
\hline
1\; 5\; 6\; 6
\end{array}
$$

1566

11 Sales of the music track 'School Rocks' fell from 8173 last week to 4238 this week. How many fewer is that?

$$
\begin{array}{r}
{}^{7}\!\not{8}\; {}^{1}1\; {}^{6}\!\not{7}\; {}^{1}3 \\
-\;4\; 2\; 3\; 8 \\
\hline
3\; 9\; 3\; 5
\end{array}
$$

3935

| How did I find Step 7? | ☐ Easy | ☐ OK | ☐ Difficult |

Step 8: Three-digit subtraction exchanging twice, adjacent digits

Sometimes, when you need to exchange twice, the two columns are next to each other. Here, the digit in the bottom number is larger than the digit above it in both the units and the tens columns.

H	T	U
5	3	4
− 1	7	8

What to do

$534 - 178 = ?$

1 You can't take 8 away from 4 so you must exchange ten from the column to its left. Cross out the 3 tens and write one fewer above it. One fewer than 3 is 2. Take the ten exchanged and write it in the units column, so instead of 4 units you now have $10 + 4 = 14$. Now subtract. $14 - 8 = 6$

H	T	U
	2	
5	3̸	¹4
− 1	7	8
		6

2 Now, move to the tens column. 7 is larger than the 2 above it so you need to exchange a hundred from the column to the left. Cross out the 5 hundreds and write one fewer above it. One fewer than 5 is 4. Think of the hundred exchanged as 10 tens and add it to the number of tens. 10 tens + 2 tens = 12 tens. $12 - 7 = 5$

H	T	U
4	12	
5̸	3̸	¹4
− 1	7	8
	5	6

3 Then complete the rest of the subtraction as normal, working from right to left. $4 - 1 = 3$

H	T	U
4	12	
5̸	3̸	¹4
− 1	7	8
3	5	6

Now you try

1

	4	16	
	5̸	7̸	¹3
−	1	9	8
	3	7	5

2

	6	14	
	7̸	5̸	¹3
−	2	7	6
	4	7	7

3

	7	14	
	8̸	5̸	¹2
−	4	9	5
	3	5	7

4

	7	11	
	8̸	2̸	¹5
−	3	7	7
	4	4	8

5

	5	14	
	6̸	5̸	¹0
−	2	5	7
	3	9	3

6

	3	17	
	4̸	8̸	¹6
−	1	9	8
	2	8	8

More practice

7
```
      3   16
   4  7̶  ¹5
 – 1  7   7
 ─────────────
   2  9   8
```

8
```
       4   12
   5̶   3̶  ¹3
 – 3   6   4
 ─────────────
   1   6   9
```

9
```
       5   11
   6̶   2̶  ¹4
 – 4   8   8
 ─────────────
   1   3   6
```

Set out these questions yourself to answer them.

10 475 – 186 = ?

H	T	U
3	16	
4̶	7̶	¹5
– 1	8	6
2	8	9

11 714 – 447 = ?

H	T	U
6	10	
7̶	1̶	¹4
– 4	4	7
2	6	7

12 730 – 187 = ?

H	T	U
6	12	
7̶	3̶	¹0
– 1	8	7
5	4	3

Problem solving

13 How many more is 674 than 287?
```
       5   16
   6̶   7̶  ¹4
 – 2   8   7
 ─────────────
   3   8   7          387
```

14 At a concert there were 734 people. If 359 were children, how many were adults?
```
       6   12
   7̶   3̶  ¹4
 – 3   5   9
 ─────────────
   3   7   5          375
```

15 There are two parcels. One weighs 872g. The other is 475g lighter. How heavy is the lighter parcel?
```
       7   16
   8̶   7̶  ¹2
 – 4   7   5
 ─────────────
   3   9   7          397g
```

16 Two numbers have a difference of 585. If the larger number is 912, what is the smaller number?
```
       8   10
   9̶   1̶  ¹2
 – 5   8   5
 ─────────────
   3   2   7          327
```

How did I find Step 8?   ☐ Easy   ☐ OK   ☐ Difficult

Step 9: Four-digit subtraction exchanging twice, adjacent digits

For questions involving four-digit numbers, work from right to left in the same way. Here, you'll need to exchange a ten and a hundred or a hundred and a thousand. Just look carefully to see when a digit is larger than the one above it.

Th	H	T	U
	7	1	2	4
−		5	7	3

What to do

$7124 - 573 = ?$

1   Start with the units. $4 - 3 = 1$

2   Move to the tens. 7 is larger than 2 so exchange from the hundreds. Cross out the 1 and write one fewer above it. One fewer than 1 is 0. Take the hundred exchanged and write it in the tens column, so instead of 2 tens, you now have 10 tens + 2 tens = 12 tens. Then subtract. $12 - 7 = 5$

Th	H	T	U
	7	1̶(0)	¹2	4
−		5	7	3
			5	1

3   Then move to the hundreds. You can't take 5 away from 0 so exchange 1 thousand. Cross out the 7 thousands and write one fewer above it. One fewer than 7 is 6. Take the thousand and write it in the hundreds column, so instead of 0 hundreds you now have 10 hundreds + 0 hundreds = 10 hundreds. $10 - 5 = 5$

Th	H	T	U
7̶(6)	1̶(10)	¹2	4
−		5	7	3
		5	5	1

4   Finally, look at the thousands column. There is nothing to subtract from the 6 thousands, so write 6 in the answer.

Th	H	T	U
7̶(6)	1̶(10)	¹2	4
−		5	7	3
6	5	5	1

Now you try

1

	5	15	
5	6̶	6̶	⁰0
−		4	8	5
5	1	7	5

2

	3	14	
4̶	5̶	¹4	6
−	1	8	7	3
2	6	7	3

3

	8	13	
9̶	4̶	¹8	8
−		9	9	7
8	4	9	1

4

	3	14	
7	4̶	5̶	¹2
−		3	9	7
7	0	5	5

More practice

Set out these questions yourself to answer them.

5 8452 – 4356 = ?

	Th	H	T	U
		3	¹4	
	8	4	5̶	¹2
–	4	3	5	6
	4	0	9	6

6 9506 – 7634 = ?

	Th	H	T	U
		8	¹4	
	9̶	5̶	¹0	6
–	7	6	3	4
	1	8	7	2

Problem solving

A palindromic number is one that reads the same forwards and backwards.

Choose two digits with a difference of 2, for example 9 and 7.
Use them to create two four-digit palindromic numbers, for example 9779 and 7997.

Use the written method to find the difference between the two numbers. Here are some examples to try. Use the grid below for working.

7 9779 – 7997 = ? _____1782_____

8 8668 – 6886 = ? _____1782_____

9 7557 – 5775 = ? _____1782_____

10 6446 – 4664 = ? _____1782_____

What do you notice about the answers? _____The answers are always 1782._____

7)

	8	16		
	9̶	7̶	¹7	9
–	7	9	9	7
	1	7	8	2

8)

	7	15		
	8	6̶	¹6	8
–	6	8	8	6
	1	7	8	2

9)

	6	14		
	7̶	5̶	¹5	7
–	5	7	7	5
	1	7	8	2

10)

	5	13		
	6̶	4̶	¹4	6
–	4	6	6	4
	1	7	8	2

How did I find Step 9?   ☐ Easy   ☐ OK   ☐ Difficult

Step 10: Four-digit subtraction with a zero in the column to be exchanged from

When there is a zero in a column that you need to exchange from, you must move further left to the next column to exchange. Notice here that that are no tens in the top number and yet you need to exchange ten.

Th	H	T	U
	6	8	0	2
−	1	3	4	5

What to do

$6802 - 1345 = ?$

Th	H	T	U
	6	8	⁷0	2
−	1	3	4	5

1 Start with the units. 5 is larger than 2 so you need to exchange from the tens. There aren't any tens! So move left and exchange from the hundreds column first. Cross out the 8 and write one fewer above it. One fewer than 8 is 7. Take the hundred exchanged and write it in the tens column, so instead of 0 tens, you now have 10 tens.

Th	H	T	U
	6	8	⁷9̶0	¹2
−	1	3	4	5
				7

2 Now go back to the units. 5 is larger than 2 so you need to exchange from the tens. Cross out the 10 and write one fewer. One fewer than 10 is 9. Write the ten exchanged as 10 units in the units column. Then subtract. $12 - 5 = 7$

Th	H	T	U
	6	8	⁷9̶0	¹2
−	1	3	4	5
	5	4	5	7

3 Then work through the rest of the subtraction, moving from right to left. For the tens, $9 - 4 = 5$. For the hundreds, $7 - 3 = 4$. For the thousands, $6 - 1 = 5$.

Now you try

1

	5	⁵6̶	⁹0̶	¹3
−	1	4	8	7
	4	1	1	6

2

	4	⁴5̶	⁹0̶	¹6
−	1	2	7	8
	3	2	2	8

3

	9	⁷8̶	⁹0̶	¹4
−	2	3	9	7
	7	4	0	7

4

	7	³4̶	⁹0̶	¹1
−	5	3	6	8
	2	0	3	3

More practice

For these questions, the zero is in the hundreds column.

5
```
       8   9
   9  ⁱ0̶  ⁱ4   8
 −  3  5   8   5
   5   4   6   3
```

6
```
       4   9
   5  ⁱ0̶  ⁱ5   9
 −  3  2   7   3
   1   7   8   6
```

7
```
       8   9
   9  ⁱ0̶  ⁱ3   6
 −  6  9   8   2
   2   0   5   4
```

8
```
       5   9
   6  ⁱ0̶  ⁱ2   8
 −  4  7   5   8
   1   2   7   0
```

Problem solving

9 At a football match there were 7304 people. If 2178 were children, how many were adults?

```
        2   9
   7  ⁱ3̶  ⁱ0̶  ⁱ4
 −  2  1   7   8
   5   1   2   6
```
5126

10 A plane flew 7055km on Monday and 2684km on Tuesday. How much further did it fly on Monday than on Tuesday?

```
        6   9
   7̶  ⁱ0̶  ⁱ5   5
 −  2  6   8   4
   4   3   7   1
```
4371km

11 A large rabbit weighs 3036g. A smaller rabbit weighs 1864g less. How much does the smaller rabbit weigh?

```
        2   9
   3̶  ⁱ0̶  ⁱ3   6
 −  1  8   6   4
   1   1   7   2
```
1172g

12 How much larger than 2548 is the number 8804?

```
        7   9
   8  8̶  ⁱ0̶  ⁱ4
 −  2  5   4   8
   6   2   5   6
```
6256

| How did I find Step 10? | ☐ Easy | ☐ OK | ☐ Difficult |

Check-up test 2 Three- and four-digit subtraction, with up to two exchanges and a zero

Step 6

1 7256 − 4324 = ?

	⁶⧸7	¹2	5	6
−	4	3	2	4
	2	9	3	2

2 6496 − 5843 = ?

	⁵⧸6	¹4	9	6
−	5	8	4	3
		6	5	3

Step 7

3 8173 − 4757 = ?

	⁷⧸8	¹1	⁶⧸7	¹3
−	4	7	5	7
	3	4	1	6

4 9390 − 3642 = ?

	⁸⧸9	¹3	⁸⧸9	¹0
−	3	6	4	2
	5	7	4	8

Step 8

5 475 − 287 = ?

	³⧸4	¹⁶⧸7	¹5
−	2	8	7
	1	8	8

6 715 − 457 = ?

	⁶⧸7	¹⁰⧸1	¹5
−	4	5	7
	2	5	8

Step 9

7 4439 − 2797 = ?

	³⧸4	¹³⧸4	¹3	9
−	2	7	9	7
	1	6	4	2

8 7452 − 367 = ?

	7	³⧸4	¹⁴⧸5	¹2
−		3	6	7
	7	0	8	5

1
2
3
4
5
6
7
8

Step 10

9 7602 – 1367 = ?

	7	6	⁵⁹̷0̸	¹2
–	1	3	6	7
	6	2	3	5

10 9037 – 7882 = ?

	⁸9̸	⁹0̸	¹3	7
–	7	8	8	2
	1	1	5	5

☐ 9

☐ 10

Steps 6 to 10 mixed

Use the grid below for working.

11 How much smaller is 4747 than 5476?

729

☐ 11

12 A TV that cost £753 was reduced by £276 in a sale. What is the sale price?

£477

☐ 12

13 Subtract 6635 from 9407.

2772

☐ 13

14 A plane travelled 8047km on Sunday and 2793km on Monday. How much further did it travel on Sunday?

5254km

☐ 14

11)

	⁴5̷	¹4	⁶7̷	¹6
–	4	7	4	7
		7	2	9

12)

	⁶7̷	¹⁴5	¹3
–	2	7	6
	4	7	7

13)

	⁸9̷	¹³4	¹0	7
–	6	6	3	5
	2	7	7	2

14)

	⁷8	⁹0̸	¹4	7
–	2	7	9	3
	5	2	5	4

Total test score

☐ / 14

Score	1	2	3	4	5	6	7	8	9	10	11	12	13	14
%	7	14	21	29	36	43	50	57	64	71	79	86	93	100

Step 11: Five-digit subtraction exchanging twice, non-adjacent digits

Work in the same way for five-digit numbers, from right to left, exchanging if you need to.

What to do

$52814 - 39371 = ?$

TTh	Th	H	T	U
		7		
5	2	8̶	¹1	4
− 3	9	3	7	1
			4	3

1 Start with the units. $4 - 1 = 3$

2 Move left to the tens. Because you can't take 7 away from 1, you must exchange a hundred from the column to its left. Cross out the 8 hundreds and write one fewer above it. One fewer than 8 is 7. Think of a hundred as 10 tens and add it to the 1 ten already there to get 11 tens. $11 - 7 = 4$

3 Then move to the hundreds. $7 - 3 = 4$

TTh	Th	H	T	U
		7		
5	2	8̶	¹1	4
− 3	9	3	7	1
		4	4	3

4 Move to the thousands. Because you can't take 9 away from 2, you must exchange a ten thousand from the column to its left. Cross out the 5 ten thousands and write one fewer above it. One fewer than 5 is 4. You now have 12 thousands. $12 - 9 = 3$

TTh	Th	H	T	U
	4		7	
5̶	¹2	8̶	¹1	4
− 3	9	3	7	1
	3	4	4	3

5 Finally, look at the ten thousands column. $4 - 3 = 1$

TTh	Th	H	T	U
	4		7	
5̶	¹2	8̶	¹1	4
− 3	9	3	7	1
1	3	4	4	3

Now you try

1

	4		6	
5̶	¹2	8	7̶	¹4
− 2	4	3	2	7
2	8	5	4	7

2

	7		4	
8	¹4	5̶	¹5	9
− 7	8	3	8	4
	6	1	7	5

3

	7		2	
9	8̶	¹2	3̶	¹3
−	4	7	1	8
9	3	5	1	5

4

	3		5	
4̶	¹5	6̶	¹3	7
− 1	7	3	4	6
2	8	2	9	1

More practice   Set out these questions yourself to answer them.

5 85 264 – 64 958 = ?

TTh	Th	H	T	U
	4		5	
8	5̶	'2	6̶	'4
– 6	4	9	5	8
2	0	3	0	6

6 83 631 – 5327 = ?

TTh	Th	H	T	U
	7		2	
8	'3	6	3̶	'1
–	5	3	2	7
	7	8	3	0	4

Problem solving

Choose two digits with a difference of 3, for example 9 and 6. Use them to create two five-digit palindromic numbers, with alternating digits, for example 96969 and 69696.

Find the differences between these numbers. Use the grid below for working.

7 96 969 – 69 696 = ?   _27 273_   **8** 85 858 – 58 585 = ?   _27 273_

9 74 747 – 47 474 = ?   _27 273_   **10** 63 636 – 36 363 = ?   _27 273_

What do you notice about the answers?   _They are always 27 273._

7)
8		8		
9̶	'6	9̶	'6	9
– 6	9	6	9	6
2	7	2	7	3

8)
7		7		
8̶	'5	8̶	'5	8
– 5	8	5	8	5
2	7	2	7	3

9)
6		6		
7̶	'4	7̶	'4	7
– 4	7	4	7	4
2	7	2	7	3

10)
5		5		
6̶	'3	6̶	'3	6
– 3	6	3	6	3
2	7	2	7	3

11 Choose two digits with a difference of 4 and explore patterns in the same way. What do you notice? Use spare paper.

The answers are always 36 364.

| **How did I find Step 11?** | ☐ Easy | ☐ OK | ☐ Difficult |

Step 12: Five-digit subtraction exchanging twice, adjacent digits

In Step 9, you subtracted four-digit numbers where you needed to exchange from two columns next to each other. Can you do the same with five-digit numbers?

TTh	Th	H	T	U
4	7	6	3	7
− 1	2	9	4	6

What to do

$47637 - 12946 = ?$

1 Start with the units. $7 - 6 = 1$

2 Move to the tens. 4 is larger than 3 so exchange from the hundreds. Cross out the 6 and write one fewer above it. One fewer than 6 is 5. Take the hundred exchanged and write it in the tens column, so instead of 3 tens you now have 10 tens + 3 tens = 13 tens. Then subtract. $13 - 4 = 9$

TTh	Th	H	T	U
			5	
4	7	6̶	¹3	7
− 1	2	9	4	6
			9	1

3 Then move to the hundreds. You can't take 9 away from 5 so exchange 1 thousand. Cross out the 7 thousands and write one fewer above it. One fewer than 7 is 6. Take the thousand and write it in the hundreds column, so instead of 5 hundreds you now have 10 hundreds + 5 hundreds = 15 hundreds. $15 - 9 = 6$

TTh	Th	H	T	U
	6	15		
4	7̶	6̶	¹3	7
− 1	2	9	4	6
		6	9	1

4 Finally, look at the thousands and then the ten thousands column and subtract. $6 - 2 = 4$ and $4 - 1 = 3$

TTh	Th	H	T	U
	6	15		
4	7̶	6̶	¹3	7
− 1	2	9	4	6
3	4	6	9	1

Now you try

1
		5	12	
8	8	6̶	3̶	¹0
− 4	3	3	4	6
4	5	2	8	4

2
		7	15	
4	8	6̶	¹1	9
− 3	2	9	4	4
1	5	6	7	5

3
	8	14		
9	5̶	4̶	6	9
− 5	7	8	3	3
3	7	6	3	6

4
	3	13		
6	4̶	4̶	¹3	7
−	2	7	6	2
6	1	6	7	5

More practice

5

```
        8   15
  8  8  9̶  6̶ '1
− 6  7  8  6  3
────────────────
  2  1  0  9  8
```

6

```
        8   10
  7  9  ¸̶  '7  8
−       6  7  9  3
────────────────
     7  2  3  8  5
```

Set out these questions yourself to answer them.

7 57 226 − 35 876 = ?

TTh	Th	H	T	U
	6	11		
5	7̶	2̶	'2	6
− 3	5	8	7	6
2	1	3	5	0

8 75 957 − 45 768 = ?

TTh	Th	H	T	U
		8	14	
7	5	9̶	5̶	'7
− 4	5	7	6	8
	3	0	1	8	9

Problem solving

9 An athletics stadium has 76 245 seats. At an athletics meeting in the stadium, 55 475 people attended. How many empty seats were there?

```
              5   11
  7  6̶  2̶  '4  5
− 5  5  4  7  5
────────────────
  2  0  7  7  0
```
20 770

10 68 753 people visited the Multiplex cinema in October. 7384 fewer than this visited in November. How many visited in November?

```
           6   14
  6  8  7̶  5̶  '3
−     7  3  8  4
────────────────
  6  1  3  6  9
```
61 369

| How did I find Step 12? | ☐ Easy | ☐ OK | ☐ Difficult |

Step 13: Five-digit subtraction with a zero in the column to be exchanged from

In Step 10, you were shown what to do with a zero in a column you needed to exchange from. These five-digit numbers have a zero in them.

What to do

$83702 - 12945 = ?$

1 Start with the units. 5 is larger than 2 so exchange from the tens. There aren't any tens! So move left and exchange from the hundreds. Cross out the 7 and write one fewer above it. One fewer than 7 is 6. Think of the hundred exchanged as 10 tens.

TTh	Th	H	T	U
		6		
8	3	7̶	'0	2
– 1	2	9	4	5

2 Now, go back to the units. 5 is larger than 2 so you need to exchange from the tens. Cross out the 10 and write one fewer above it. One fewer than 10 is 9. Write the ten as 10 units in the units column. Then subtract the units and the tens. $12 - 5 = 7$ and $9 - 4 = 5$

		6	9	
8	3	7̶	0̶	'2
– 1	2	9	4	5
			5	7

3 Then work through the rest of the subtraction, moving from right to left. Watch out for any other exchanging needed. Here, as you can't take 9 hundreds from the 6 hundreds, exchange from the thousands. For the hundreds, $16 - 9 = 7$. For the thousands, $2 - 2 = 0$. For the ten thousands, $8 - 1 = 7$.

	2	16	9	
8	3̶	7̶	0̶	'2
– 1	2	9	4	5
7	0	7	5	7

Now you try

1

	5	9	
7	3	6̶	'0	'2
– 5	2	3	4	9
2	1	2	5	3

2

	4	9	
8	5̶	0̶	'3	7
– 2	2	3	7	5
6	2	6	6	2

3

2	12	9	
6	3̶	3̶	0̶	'3
– 5	2	7	2	8
1	0	5	7	5

4

6	5	9	
7̶	'2	6̶	0̶	'5
– 3	6	3	7	9
3	6	2	2	6

More practice

5
```
      8  9
  9 ⁸0¹4  8  7
−  4  6  8  6  5
─────────────────
   4  3  6  2  2
```

6
```
      7  ¹⁴ 9
  8  5 ⁴0¹1  8
−  3  7  3  7  4
─────────────────
   4  7  6  4  4
```

7
```
      5      3  9
  ⁶0¹0  4 ⁴0¹7
−  5  6  3  7  9
─────────────────
   4  0  2  8
```

8
```
         5  9
  8  9  6 ⁶0¹3
−        7  5  8  4
─────────────────
   8  2  0  1  9
```

Problem solving

9 A forestry service planted 50 364 trees last year but cut down 36 762 trees. How many more trees were planted than were cut down?

```
     4  9
 5 ⁴0¹3  6  4
− 3  6  7  6  2
──────────────
 1  3  6  0  2
```
13 602

10 On a hillside in a nature reserve 37 674 butterflies were counted in June. In July, 41 056 were counted. How many more were counted in July than in June?

```
     3  10 9
 4  ¹1 ⁴0¹5  6
− 3  7  6  7  4
──────────────
    3  3  8  2
```
3382

11 Find the difference between 40 694 and 27 751.

```
     3  9
 4 ⁴0¹6  9  4
− 2  7  7  5  1
──────────────
 1  2  9  4  3
```
12 943

12 Gita, a bank clerk, earns £33 773 per year. Her boss earns £84 059. How much more does her boss earn than Gita?

```
        3  9
 8  4 ⁴0¹5  9
− 3  3  7  7  3
──────────────
 5  0  2  8  6
```
£50 286

How did I find Step 13?   ☐ Easy   ☐ OK   ☐ Difficult

Step 14: Five-digit subtraction exchanging three or four times

Now that you are confident in exchanging twice, you can easily exchange three or more times!

What to do

$72642 - 39768 = ?$

1 Start with the units. 8 is larger than 2 so exchange from the tens. $12 - 8 = 4$

TTh	Th	H	T	U
			5	13
7	2	6	4̶	¹2
− 3	9	7	6	8
			7	4

2 Move to the tens. 6 is larger than 3 so exchange from the hundreds. $13 - 6 = 7$

TTh	Th	H	T	U
	1	15	13	
7	2̶	6̶	4̶	¹2
− 3	9	7	6	8
		8	7	4

3 Then move to the hundreds. 7 is larger than 5 so exchange from the thousands. $15 - 7 = 8$

TTh	Th	H	T	U
6	11	15	13	
7̶	2̶	6̶	4̶	¹2
− 3	9	7	6	8
	2	8	7	4

4 Move to the thousands. 9 is larger than 1 so exchange from the ten thousands. $11 - 9 = 2$

TTh	Th	H	T	U
6	11	15	13	
7̶	2̶	6̶	4̶	¹2
− 3	9	7	6	8
3	2	8	7	4

5 Finally, look at the ten thousands and subtract. $6 - 3 = 3$

Now you try

1

		8	15	12
7	9	6̶	3̶	¹0
− 4	8	7	4	8
3	0	8	8	2

2

	6	10		5
7̶	1̶	¹5	6̶	¹4
−	6	9	4	7
6	4	6	1	7

3

	8	14	13	15
9	5̶	4̶	6̶	¹1
− 5	7	8	7	8
3	7	5	8	3

4

	7	15	15	15
8	6̶	6̶	6̶	¹7
− 4	8	7	6	9
3	7	8	9	8

5

	4		3		14
	5	⁵5	4	⁵5	¹3
−	2	8	0	9	5
	2	7	3	5	8

6

		7	11		14
	8	⁷2	5	¹3	7
−	4	2	8	6	3
	3	9	6	7	4

More practice   Set out these questions yourself to answer them.

7   57 251 − 35 876 = ?

TTh	Th	H	T	U
	6	11	14	
5	⁷7	⁸2	⁵5	¹1
− 3	5	8	7	6
2	1	3	7	5

8   82 514 − 5768 = ?

TTh	Th	H	T	U
	7	11	14	10
8	⁸2	⁵5	¹1	¹4
−		5	7	6	8
7	6	7	4	6

9   11 111 − 8888 = ?

TTh	Th	H	T	U
0	10	10	10	
¹1	¹1	¹1	¹1	¹1
−		8	8	8	8
	2	2	2	3

10   51 506 − 26 764 = ?

TTh	Th	H	T	U
	4	10	14	
⁵5	¹1	⁵5	¹0	6
− 2	6	7	6	4
2	4	7	4	2

Problem solving

11   A music arena has 55 377 seats. At the concert on Saturday there were 8489 empty seats. How many seats were not empty?

	4	14	12	16	
⁵5	⁵5	³3	⁷7	¹7
−		8	4	8	9
4	6	8	8	8

46 888

12   Find the difference between each pair of numbers. Use spare paper for working.

a 55 555 and 7777 ___47 778___   **b** 44 444 and 6666 ___37 778___

c 33 333 and 5555 ___27 778___   **d** 22 222 and 4444 ___17 778___

| **How did I find Step 14?** | ☐ Easy | ☐ OK | ☐ Difficult |

Step 15: Five-digit subtraction with zeros in the columns to be exchanged from

In Step 13, you saw what to do with a zero in a column you had to exchange from. These numbers have several zeros.

What to do

$87002 - 12478 = ?$

	TTh	Th	H	T	U
		6			
	8	$\not{7}$	^{1}0	0	2
−	1	2	4	7	8

1. Start with the units. 8 is larger than 2 so exchange from the tens. There aren't any tens! So move left and exchange from the hundreds. There aren't any hundreds! So move left and exchange from the thousands. Cross out the 7 and write 6 above. Think of the thousand exchanged as 10 hundreds.

		6	9		
	8	$\not{7}$	$\not{0}$	^{1}0	2
−	1	2	4	7	8

2. Now, exchange from the hundreds as there are 10 now. Cross out the 10 hundreds and write one fewer. One fewer than 10 is 9. Think of the hundred exchanged as 10 tens.

		6	9	9	
	8	$\not{7}$	$\not{0}$	$\not{0}$	^{1}2
−	1	2	4	7	8
					4

3. Go back to the units. 8 is larger than 2 so exchange from the tens. Cross out the 10 tens and write one fewer. One fewer than 10 is 9. Write the ten as 10 units in the units column. Then subtract. $12 - 8 = 4$

		6	9	9	
	8	$\not{7}$	$\not{0}$	$\not{0}$	^{1}2
−	1	2	4	7	8
	7	4	5	2	4

4. Work through the rest of the subtraction, moving from right to left. For the tens, $9 - 7 = 2$. For the hundreds, $9 - 4 = 5$. For the thousands, $6 - 2 = 4$. For the ten thousands, $8 - 1 = 7$.

Now you try

1

		8	9	9	
	8	$\not{9}$	$\not{0}$	$\not{0}$	^{1}2
−	7	2	3	4	9
	1	6	6	5	3

2

		4	9	9	
	5	$\not{0}$	$\not{0}$	^{1}4	8
−	2	2	3	7	5
	2	7	6	7	3

3

		2	9	9	
	7	3	$\not{0}$	$\not{0}$	^{1}3
−	5	2	7	2	8
	2	0	2	7	5

4

		5	9	9	9
	6	$\not{0}$	$\not{0}$	$\not{0}$	^{1}5
−	3	6	3	7	9
	2	3	6	2	6

More practice

5
```
      8  9  9
   9  ⁰0 ⁰0 ¹3  7
 -    7  6  8  7  5
   1  3  1  6  2
```

6
```
         7  ¹4  9
      8  5  ⁰0 ¹0  8
 -    5  8  3  7  3
      2  6  6  3  5
```

Problem solving

7 In one year 70 047 people visited a tourist attraction in London. If 35 486 of them were adults, how many were children?

```
      6   9   9
   ⁷7  ⁰0  ⁰0  ¹4  7
 -  3  5   4   8   6
    3  4   5   6   1
```
34 561

8 Efia won £62 002 in the lottery. She gave £47 463 of it to charity. How much did she keep for herself?

```
      5  ¹1  9   9
   ⁶6  ⁸2  ⁰0  ⁰0  ¹2
 -  4   7   4   6   3
    1   4   5   3   9
```
£14 539

9 Find the difference between 40 004 and 33 333.

```
      3   9   9
   ⁴4  ⁰0  ⁰0  ¹0  4
 -  3   3   3   3   3
        6   6   7   1
```
6671

10 A rescue centre helped a total of 32 008 dogs last year. They found 29 453 of them homes. How many didn't they find a home for?

```
      2  ¹1  9
   ³3  ²2  ⁰0  ¹0  8
 -  2   9   4   5   3
        2   5   5   5
```
2555

11 Jan earned £30 006 last year. He paid £8536 in tax and spent the rest. How much did he spend?

```
      2   9   9
   ³3  ⁰0  ⁰0  ¹0  6
 -      8   5   3   6
    2   1   4   7   0
```
£21 470

| How did I find Step 15? | ☐ Easy | ☐ OK | ☐ Difficult |

Check-up test 3 Five-digit subtraction, with several exchanges and zeros

Step 11

1 64 732 – 55 317 = ?

	6⁵	¹4	7	3²	¹2
–	5	5	3	1	7
		9	4	1	5

2 60 638 – 17 587 = ?

	6⁵	¹0	6⁵	¹3	8
–	1	7	5	8	7
	4	3	0	5	1

Step 12

3 64 438 – 41 972 = ?

	6	4³	4¹³	¹3	8
–	4	1	9	7	2
	2	2	4	6	6

4 75 954 – 33 257 = ?

	7	5	9⁸	5¹⁴	¹4
–	3	3	2	5	7
	4	2	6	9	7

Step 13

5 95 039 – 21 375 = ?

	9	5	0⁴	¹3⁹	9
–	2	1	3	7	5
	7	3	6	6	4

6 60 403 – 28 329 = ?

	6⁵	¹0	4	0³	¹3⁹
–	2	8	3	2	9
	3	2	0	7	4

Step 14

7 95 463 – 47 588 = ?

	9⁸	5¹⁴	4¹³	6¹⁵	¹3
–	4	7	5	8	8
	4	7	8	7	5

8 85 151 – 29 075 = ?

	8⁷	¹5	1⁰	5¹⁴	¹1
–	2	9	0	7	5
	5	6	0	7	6

Step 15

9 93006 − 51149 = ?

		2	9	9	
	9	3	0̸	0̸	ⁱ6
−	5	1	1	4	9
	4	1	8	5	7

10 90007 − 36379 = ?

		8	9	9	9	
	9̸	0̸	0̸	0̸	ⁱ7
−	3	6	3	7	9
	5	3	6	2	8

□ 9
□ 10

Steps 11 to 15 mixed

Use the grids below for working.

11 A rugby stadium has 58382 seats. At the match on Saturday there were 18649 empty seats. How many seats were occupied?

39733

□ 11

12 Find the difference between 52694 and 27751.

24943

□ 12

		4	17		7	
11)	5̸	8̸	ⁱ3	8̸	ⁱ2
	−	1	8	6	4	9
		3	9	7	3	3

		4	11			
12)	5̸	2̸	ⁱ6	9	4
	−	2	7	7	5	1
		2	4	9	4	3

13 Simon, an IT manager, earns £33673 per year. His boss earns £84009. How much more than Simon does his boss earn?

£50336

□ 13

14 Subtract 37073 from 73037.

35964

□ 14

			3	9		
13)	8	4	0̸	ⁱ0	9
	−	3	3	6	7	3
		5	0	3	3	6

			6	12	9	
14)	7̸	3̸	0̸	ⁱ3	7
	−	3	7	0	7	3
		3	5	9	6	4

Total test score

Score	1	2	3	4	5	6	7	8	9	10	11	12	13	14
%	7	14	21	29	36	43	50	57	64	71	79	86	93	100

14

Step 16: Large number subtraction

What to do

1 You've learnt how to do written subtraction for up to five-digit numbers. Subtracting even larger numbers is just as easy!

2 Just remember to exchange where needed.

HTh	TTh	Th	H	T	U
4	9		5	13	
5	ⁱ0	ⁱ6	8	4	ⁱ1
− 2	4	8	2	7	3
2	5	8	3	6	8

Now you try

1 Seven hundred and nine thousand, three hundred and seventeen minus thirty-one thousand, four hundred and forty-six.

	6		8	12		
	7	ⁱ0	9	3	ⁱ1	7
−		3	1	4	4	6
	6	7	7	8	7	1

2 Nine hundred and twenty thousand, three hundred and fifty subtract six hundred and eighty-two thousand and eighteen.

		8		11		4	
	9	2	ⁱ0	3	5	ⁱ0
−	6	8	2	0	1	8
	2	3	8	3	3	2

3 Eight hundred thousand, five hundred and twelve minus two hundred and sixty thousand, two hundred and nineteen.

	7			4	10		
	8	ⁱ0	0	5	1	ⁱ2
−	2	6	0	2	1	9
	5	4	0	2	9	3

4 Two hundred and sixty-one thousand nine hundred and three subtract ninety-four thousand, six hundred and seven.

	1	15		8	9		
	2	6	ⁱ1	9	0	ⁱ3
−		9	4	6	0	7
	1	6	7	2	9	6

5 Six hundred and ninety thousand and thirty minus seventy-eight thousand, two hundred and forty-one.

		8	9	9	12		
	6	9	ⁱ0	ⁱ0	3	ⁱ0
−		7	8	2	4	1
	6	1	1	7	8	9

6 Five hundred and twelve thousand and forty-two subtract two hundred and six thousand and sixty-five.

		0	11	9	13		
	5	1	2	ⁱ0	4	ⁱ2
−	2	0	6	0	6	5
	3	0	5	9	7	7

More practice

Set out these questions yourself to answer them.

7 Six hundred and twenty-six thousand, four hundred and three take away four hundred and eighty-six thousand, six hundred and nine.

HTh	TTh	Th	H	T	U
5	11	15	13	9	
6̶	2̶	6̶	4̶	⁹0̶	¹3
− 4	8	6	6	0	9
1	3	9	7	9	4

8 Two hundred and fifty thousand and seventeen take away eighty-nine thousand, four hundred and eight.

HTh	TTh	Th	H	T	U
1	14	9		0	
2̶	5	0̶	¹0	1̶	¹7
−	8	9	4	0	8
1	6	0	6	0	9

Problem solving

9 A group of people raised £385 057 for two charities. They gave £184 488 to one charity. How much did they give to the other?

```
      4  9  14
   3 8 5̶ 0̶ 5̶ ¹7
 − 1 8 4  4  8  8
   2 0 0  5  6  9
```
£200 569

10 There were 573 684 people at an Olympic event. If 375 427 of them were female, how many were male?

```
   4   16      7
   5̶ 7̶ ¹3 6 8̶ ¹4
 − 3 7  5 4 2  7
   1 9  8 2 5  7
```
198 257

11 Find the difference between two palindromic six-digit numbers that can be made with the digits 3 and 7, for example 737 737 subtract 377 773. Try different ways, working on the grid or using spare paper.

Can you find a question with the answer 435 644?

773 377 − 337 733

Step 17: Decimal subtraction two decimal places

Now that you can subtract whole numbers, subtracting decimals is almost as easy! All you need to do is to set out the digits in the correct columns and subtract in the same way!

What to do

$34.56 - 8.47 = ?$

1 Start with the right-hand column. Because you can't take 7 away from 6, you must exchange from the column to its left. Cross out the 5 tenths and write one fewer above it. One fewer than 5 is 4. Think of the tenth as 10 hundredths and add it to the 6 hundredths. $16 - 7 = 9$

H	T	U	.	t	h
	3	4	.	$\overset{4}{\cancel{5}}$	^{16}
−		8	.	4	7
					9

2 Then move to the tenths. $4 - 4 = 0$

	3	4	.	$\overset{4}{\cancel{5}}$	^{16}
−		8	.	4	7
				0	9

3 Continue working from right to left to complete the subtraction.

4 Remember to put the decimal point in your answer, in line with the decimal points above.

	$\overset{2}{\cancel{3}}$	$^1\overset{4}{\cancel{4}}$	.	$\overset{4}{\cancel{5}}$	^{16}
−		8	.	4	7
	2	6	.	0	9

Now you try

1 $519.74 - 43.27 = ?$

	5	^{1}1	9	.	$\overset{6}{\cancel{7}}$	^{14}
−		4	3	.	2	7
	4	7	6	.	4	7

(above the 1 is a small 4; above the 7 a small 6)

2 $45.59 - 7.84 = ?$

		$\overset{3}{\cancel{4}}$	5	.	$^1\cancel{5}$	9
−			7	.	8	4
		3	7	.	7	5

3 $352.74 - 127.83 = ?$

	3	$\overset{4}{\cancel{5}}$	$^{11}\cancel{2}$	.	7	4
−	1	2	7	.	8	3
	2	2	4	.	9	1

4 $50.43 - 13.79 = ?$

	5	$\overset{4}{\cancel{0}}$	.	$\overset{9}{\cancel{4}}$	$^{13}\cancel{3}$
−	1	3	.	7	9
	3	6	.	6	4

More practice

Set out these questions yourself to answer them.

5 852.64 – 649.58 = ?

H	T	U	.	t	h
	⁴		.	⁵	
8	5̶	'2	.	6̶	'4
– 6	4	9	.	5	8
2	0	3	.	0	6

6 836.31 – 53.27 = ?

H	T	U	.	t	h
	⁷		.	²	
8̶	'3	6	.	3̶	'1
–	5	3	.	2	7
7	8	3	.	0	4

Problem solving

7 Jo runs 56.72km in January and 64.18km in February. How much further does she run in February?

```
      ⁵  ¹³
      6̶  4̶ . 1  8
   –  5  6 . 7  2
      ─────────────
         7 . 4  6
```
7.46km

8 Jack wants to buy a laptop costing £746.45. He already has £673.83. How much more does he need to save?

```
      ⁶     ⁵
      7̶ '4  6̶ . '4  5
   –  6  7  3 . 8   3
      ──────────────────
         7  2 . 6   2
```
£72.62

9 Charlie weighed 90.48kg before a diet. After a diet his weight had fallen to 74.73kg. How much weight had he lost?

```
      ⁸  ⁹
      9̶ 0̶ . '4  8
   –  7  4 . 7   3
      ───────────────
      1  5 . 7   5
```
15.75kg

| **How did I find Step 17?** | Easy | OK | ☐ Difficult |

Step 18: Decimal subtraction different numbers of decimal places

What to do

In this last step, the questions have different numbers of decimal places so you must be careful to write the digits in the correct columns. Sometimes it can help to write zeros into the empty spaces. Don't forget to put the decimal point in your answer each time!

Now you try
Set out these questions yourself to answer them.

1   492.76 – 16.825 = ?

H	T	U . t	h	th
	8	11	5	
4	9	2 . 7	6 '0	
–	1	6 . 8	2	5
4	7	5 . 9	3	5

2   205.7 – 52.139 = ?

H	T	U . t	h	th
	1	6	9	
2 '0	5 . 7	'0	'0	
–	5	2 . 1	3	9
1	5	3 . 5	6	1

3   842.9 – 9.82 = ?

H	T	U . t	h
	3	8	
8	4 '2 . 9	'0	
–		9 . 8	2
8	3	3 . 0	8

4   78.135 – 38.66 = ?

H	T	U . t	h	th
	6	17	10	
7	8 . 1	'3	5	
–	3	8 . 6	6	0
3	9 . 4	7	5	

More practice
Set out these questions yourself to answer them.

5   900.8 – 174.631 = ?

H	T	U . t	h	th
8	9	7	9	
9	'0 '0 . 8	'0	'0	
– 1	7	4 . 6	3	1
7	2	6 . 1	6	9

6   801.3 – 562.49 = ?

H	T	U . t	h
7	9	10	12
8	'0	1 . 3	'0
–	5	6	2 . 4	9
2	3	8 . 8	1

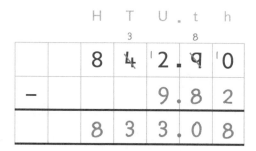

Problem solving

Check your answers by adding.

7 Two large crates weigh 406.9kg and 384.73kg. How much heavier is one crate than the other?

```
    3          8
  4 '0  6. 9 '0
-  3 8  4. 7  3
        2 2 . 1  7
```

22.17kg

8 A baby weighed 3.46kg at birth. At six months old he weighed 7.257kg. How much weight had he gained?

```
      6   11
  7 . 2  '5  7
-  3 . 4  6  0
   3 . 7  9  7
```

3.797kg

9 A river is 7.84m wide at its narrowest point and 204.9m wide at its widest point. How much wider is it at its widest point than at its narrowest point?

```
    1   9      8
  2 '0  4. 9 '0
-        7. 8  4
  1 9  7. 0  6
```

197.06m

10 What is 30.08ml less than 125ml?

```
  0       4   9
  1 '2  5. 0 '0
-      3 0. 0  8
    9 4. 9  2
```

94.92ml

11 Ali took £278 spending money on holiday. On the first week of his holiday he spent £183.67. How much did he have left for the second week?

```
    1       7   9
  2 '7  8. 0 '0
-  1 8  3. 6  7
    9 4. 3  3
```

£94.33

12 Usain Bolt ran 100m in 9.572 seconds. How much faster did he run than the 1891 world record holder who ran it in 10.8 seconds?

```
  0       7   9
  1 '0 . 8  0 '0
-    9 . 5  7  2
     1 . 2  2  8
```

1.228 secs

| How did I find Step 18? | ☐ Easy | ☐ OK | ☐ Difficult |

Final test Subtraction of whole numbers and decimals

Steps 16 to 18

1   Nine hundred and twenty thousand, three hundred and fifty take away six hundred and eighty-two thousand and eighteen.

	⁸ 9	¹¹ 2	'0	3	⁴ 5	'0
−	6	8	2	0	1	8
	2	3	8	3	3	2

2   Seven hundred and twenty thousand and seventeen take away four hundred and forty-six thousand, six hundred and two.

	⁶ 7	¹¹ 2	⁹ 0	'0	1	7
−	4	4	6	6	0	2
	2	7	3	4	1	5

☐ 1
☐ 2

3   567.27 − 164.58 = ?

	5	6	⁶ 7 .	¹¹ 2	'7
−	1	6	4 .	5	8
	4	0	2 .	6	9

4   828.36 − 55.29 = ?

	⁷ 8	'2	8 .	² 3	'6
−		5	5 .	2	9
	7	7	3 .	0	7

☐ 3
☐ 4

5   742.9 − 16.826 = ?

	7	³ 4	'2 .	⁸ 9	⁹ 0	'0
−		1	6 .	8	2	6
	7	2	6 .	0	7	4

6   55.134 − 28.77 = ?

	5	5 .	⁴ 1	¹⁴ 3	¹⁰ 4
−	2	8 .	7	7	0
	2	6 .	3	6	4

☐ 5
☐ 6

Use the grid below for working.

7   Subtract 90.92 from 902.9.   811.98

8   What is 42.15g less than 153g?   110.85g

☐ 7
☐ 8

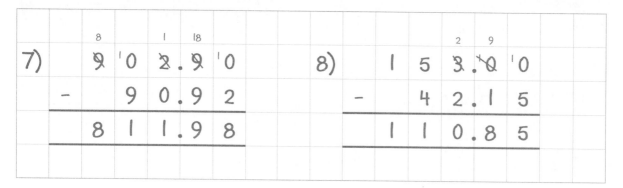

7)		⁸ 9	'0	¹ 2 .	¹⁸ 9	'0		8)		1	5	² 3 .	⁹ 0	'0
	−		9	0 .	9	2			−			4	2 .	1	5
		8	1	1 .	9	8					1	1	0 .	8	5

Steps 1 to 18 mixed

Use the grid below for working.

9 Two numbers have a difference of 733. If the larger number is 961, what is the smaller number?

228

10 Monika had £6747 in a bank account. She took out £1824 to buy a car. How much money is left in the account?

£4923

11 Find the difference between 8338 and 3883.

4455

12 How much larger is 45006 than 38574?

6432

13 A puppy weighs 9036g. When it was born it weighed 5864g less. How much did it weigh when it was born?

3172g

14 A forestry service planted 50687 trees last year but cut down 36779 trees. How many more trees were planted than were cut down?

13908

9)
```
        5
    9   6  ¹1
 -  7   3   3
 ─────────────
    2   2   8
```

10)
```
        5
    6  ¹7   4   7
 -  1   8   2   4
 ──────────────────
    4   9   2   3
```

11)
```
    7  12
    8   3  ¹3   8
 -  3   8   8   3
 ──────────────────
    4   4   5   5
```

12)
```
        3   14   9
    4   5  ¹0  ¹0   6
 -  3   8   5    7   4
 ──────────────────────
        6   4    3   2
```

13)
```
    8   9
    9  ¹0  ¹3   6
 -  5   8   6   4
 ──────────────────
    3   1   7   2
```

14)
```
    4   9        7
    5  ¹0  ¹6   8  ¹7
 -  3   6   7   7   9
 ──────────────────────
    1   3   9   0   8
```

Total test score

Score	1	2	3	4	5	6	7	8	9	10	11	12	13	14
%	7	14	21	29	36	43	50	57	64	71	79	86	93	100

14

Written Calculation

Group record sheet

Pupil Book: _____

Class/Set: _____

Pupil's name	Check-up test 1	Check-up test 2	Check-up test 3	Final test	Assessment test 1*	Assessment test 2*	Mixed calculations test*

*Available as assessment resources in the back of the **Written Calculation: Teacher's Guide** (ISBN 978 07217 1278 9)

From: **Written Calculation: Subtraction Answers** by Hilary Koll and Steve Mills (ISBN 978 07217 1273 4). Copyright © Schofield & Sims Ltd, 2015. Published by Schofield & Sims Ltd, Dogley Mill, Fenay Bridge, Huddersfield HD8 0NQ, UK (www.schofieldandsims.co.uk). This page may be photocopied after purchase for use within your school or institution only.